Magical Designs Coloring Art Book
100 Hand-Drawn Inspirations ~ Volume 1

DOODLE ART ALLEY BOOKS
Samantha Snyder

Magical Designs Coloring Art Book is available at special discounts when purchased
in quantities for educational use, fundraising, or sales promotions.
For more information, contact: info@akabooks.com

Cover images © 2015 by Doodle Art Alley.

ISBN-13: 978-0983918288
ISBN-10: 0983918287

This edition is published by aka Associates.
www.akabooks.com

Doodle Art Alley Books

CONTENTS

INTRODUCTION

Hi everyone!

My name is Samantha and I've been doodling ever since I was a kid. I never thought too much of my doodle creations until I became an elementary school teacher. I was so excited to share my love of making art for my students, but I found that the kids were easily frustrated by their lack of creative confidence. I started drawing up coloring pages and activity sheets and their attitudes changed dramatically. With a little push, they started creating their own artwork that they could be proud of.

Those few coloring printables I drew up back in 2008 turned into the start of Doodle Art Alley, my website dedicated to Doodle art and the joys that come from it. Over the years I have heard from many people, sharing their experiences with me about my coloring pages, many of them educators and therapists. I learned that my coloring art pages were more than a fun way to pass the time.

Mental Discipline – Coloring can help out attention, leading to greater focus and dedication. We also develop patience. So often we are in a hurry to get to the destination, we don't enjoy the journey. Slow down and enjoy the colors and patterns coming to life in front of you.

Relaxation – Coloring is a great way to relax. Take a deep breath, sit down and color. Let the detailed designs take shape before your eyes. Take in what's being created right in front of you and appreciate it for the beauty it is. You'll find yourself relaxed and at ease.

Creation – You aren't just coloring, you are creating art. You carefully choose your color combinations and what patterns they create. Taking your time and using your own innate creative talent, you will produce your own piece of art, something you can be proud of and share with others. Creating is a wonderful accomplishment that boosts confidence and belief in yourself.

Fun – It's simple. Coloring is fun. It is something we discover as a child that never leaves us. While coloring can be an individual activity, encouraging meditation and relaxation, it is also an activity that brings family and friends together. Teachers chatting around a table during their conference time, friends gossiping at a sleepover, students joking in their dorm room, and family members reminiscing at a reunion, all coloring and creating art.

So come explore some doodle art! A quick glance at a doodle may show scribbles, random lines and shapes with no meaning or significance. However, with a little love and direction, these drawings have the potential to compete with some of the best artwork there is! Doodling is so much more than simply drawing on a post-it or unconsciously scribbling on your notebook paper during an especially boring lecture. With the right care and approach, beautiful pictures can be created. Geometric and abstract designs along with wonderfully detailed artwork can grow from one simple, single line. Even emotional and mental healing can stem from a tiny little mark. The ideas and creative pathways are endless.

Doodle Art Alley is dedicated to giving those squiggly lines the proper credit they deserve. Who would have thought that such a small and simple idea could possess so much potential? Go on and explore the magic of the doodle!

Enjoy!

Samantha

ABSTRACT DESIGNS

Doodle Art Alley ©

Doodle Art Alley ©

Doodle Art Alley ©

Doodle Art Alley ©

Doodle Art Alley ©

Doodle Art Alley ©

Doodle Art Alley ©

Doodle Art Alley ©

Doodle Art Alley ©

Doodle Art Alley ©

Doodle Art Alley ©

Doodle Art Alley ©

Doodle Art Alley ©

Doodle Art Alley ©

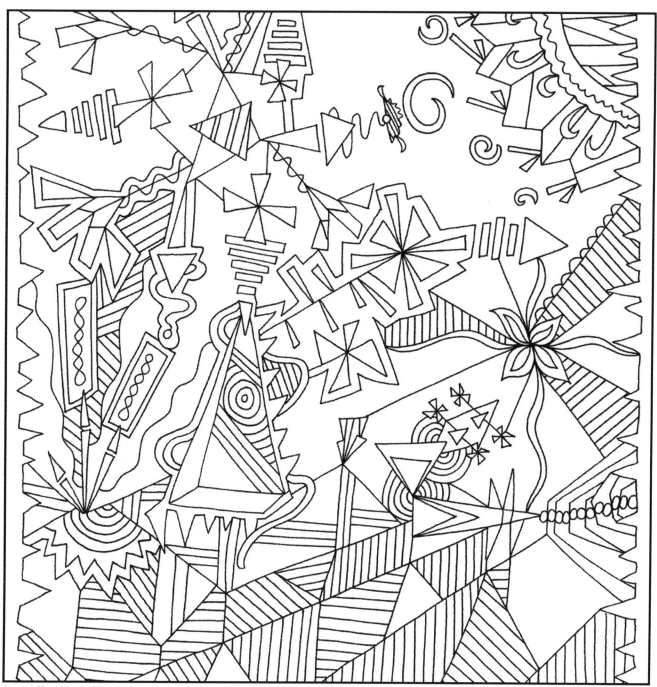

Doodle Art Alley ©

Doodle Art Alley ©

Doodle Art Alley ©

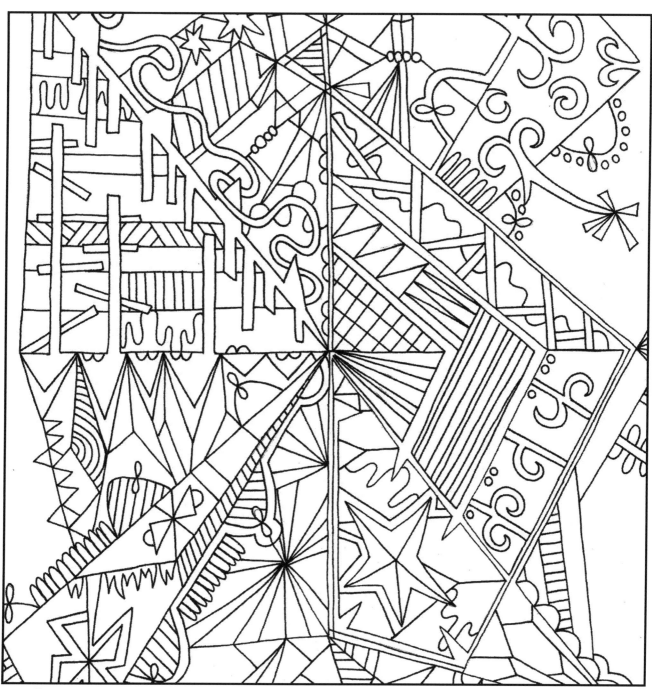

Doodle Art Alley ©

ANIMAL DESIGNS

Doodle Art Alley ©

Doodle Art Alley ©

Doodle Art Alley ©

Doodle Art Alley ©

Doodle Art Alley ©

Doodle Art Alley ©

GEOMETRIC DESIGNS

Doodle Art Alley ©

Doodle Art Alley ©

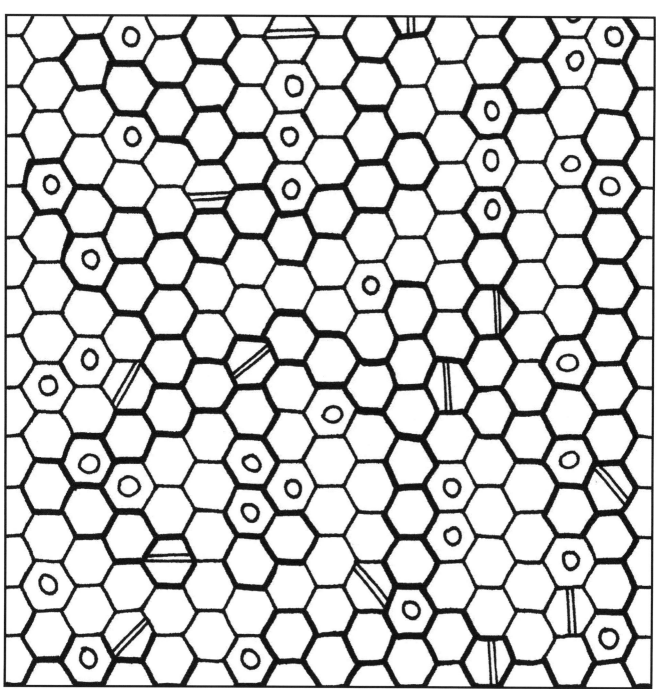

Doodle Art Alley ©

Doodle Art Alley ©

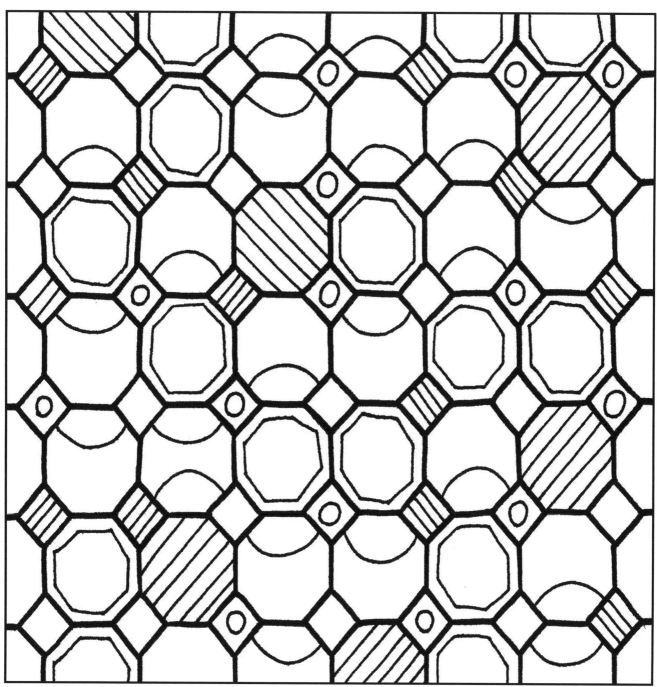

Doodle Art Alley ©

Doodle Art Alley ©

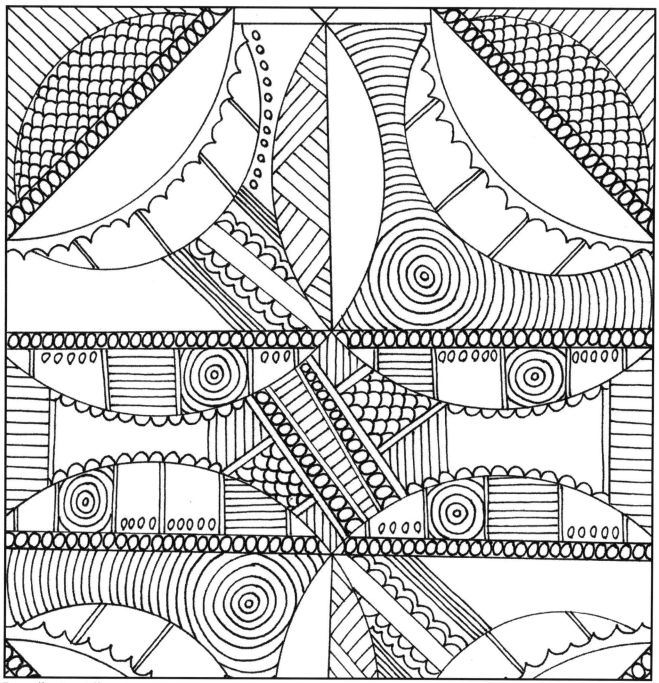

Doodle Art Alley ©

Doodle Art Alley ©

Doodle Art Alley ©

Doodle Art Alley ©

Doodle Art Alley ©

HENNA DESIGNS

Doodle Art Alley ©

Doodle Art Alley ©

Doodle Art Alley ©

Doodle Art Alley ©

Doodle Art Alley ©

Doodle Art Alley ©

Doodle Art Alley ©

Doodle Art Alley ©

Doodle Art Alley ©

Doodle Art Alley ©

MANDALA DESIGNS

Doodle Art Alley ©

Doodle Art Alley ©

Doodle Art Alley ©

Doodle Art Alley ©

Doodle Art Alley ©

Doodle Art Alley ©

Doodle Art Alley ©

Doodle Art Alley ©

Doodle Art Alley ©

Doodle Art Alley ©

Doodle Art Alley ©

Doodle Art Alley ©

Doodle Art Alley ©

Doodle Art Alley ©

Doodle Art Alley ©

Doodle Art Alley ©

NATURE DESIGNS

Doodle Art Alley ©

Doodle Art Alley ©

Doodle Art Alley ©

Doodle Art Alley ©

Doodle Art Alley ©

Doodle Art Alley ©

Doodle Art Alley ©

Doodle Art Alley ©

Doodle Art Alley ©

Doodle Art Alley ©

Doodle Art Alley ©

SPACE DESIGNS

Doodle Art Alley ©

Doodle Art Alley ©

Doodle Art Alley ©

Doodle Art Alley ©

Doodle Art Alley ©

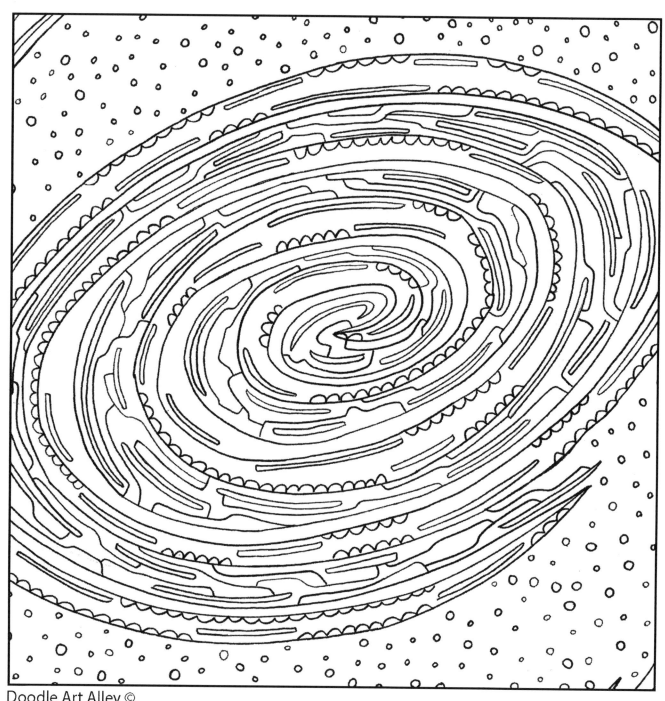

Doodle Art Alley ©

Doodle Art Alley ©

Doodle Art Alley ©

ABOUT DOODLE ART ALLEY

Samantha Snyder has been doodling her whole life. While teaching elementary school, she often drew up coloring pages and printables for her students and fellow teachers. She decided to start sharing her creations and in 2008, Doodle Art Alley was founded.

A quick glance at a doodle may show scribbles, random lines and shapes with no meaning or significance. However, with a little love and direction, these drawings have the potential to compete with some of the best artwork there is!

Doodle Art Alley is dedicated to giving those squiggly lines the proper credit they deserve. Who would have thought that such a small and simple idea could possess so much potential?

There are lots of fun doodle art activities, tips, and information to read through and enjoy. Visit www.doodle-art-alley.com for hundreds of exciting doodles.

Doodle Art Alley Books

Made in the USA
San Bernardino, CA
24 August 2016